Under the Skin

Badger Plays Book 6

ICE MAIDEN

and Under the Skin

D0808215

Mike Gould

Contents:

Sykes and the Warden rule the estate. But then Sykes gets a message to go and see 'The Girl' living in the basement. The girl talked about by many, but never seen. Sykes bullies Linus into coming with him, but when they arrive in the ice maiden's room, a surprise awaits. And the Warden is never far behind, wanting to know what's going on...

Lena's friends invite her to share in a tattoo to commemorate their friendship, but Lena's not sure if she wants to. But how do you refuse a powerful mate such as Su, a girl you practically consider your sister?

Under the Skin - *The Plays:*

Book 1: Louise Loxton   Night Caller, The Gift, Boys Behaving Badly, Sleeping Easy, Bath Time

Book 2: Mike Gould   Ring of Blood, Animal Magic, Eco-freaks in Trouble, The Case of the Following Boy, The Sub

Book 3: Rob Brannen   Hedge Hopping, Sorting Things Out, Michael and Rahima, Into the Dark, A Swagger and A Snarl

Book 4: Mike Gould   Ten Things I Hate, Joker in the Pack, Dial-a-date, Masked Ball, The First Girl in Space

Book 5: Dick Kempson   Conquistador, The Boy at the Hotel Rudolpho

Book 6: Mike Gould   Ice Maiden, Under the Skin

Badger Publishing Limited 15 Wedgwood Gate, Pin Green Industrial Estate, Stevenage, Hertfordshire SG1 4SU
Telephone: 01438 356907.   Fax: 01438 747015.
www.badger-publishing.co.uk   enquiries@badger-publishing.co.uk

Under the Skin - Book 6   ISBN 1 84424 433 4

Text © Mike Gould 2005
Series editing © Mike Gould 2005
Complete work © Badger Publishing Limited 2005

All rights reserved. No part of this publication may be reproduced, stored in any form or by any means mechanical, electronic, recording or otherwise without the prior permission of the publisher.

The right of Mike Gould to be identified as author of this Work has been asserted by him in accordance with the Copyright, Designs and Patents Act 1988.

Series Editor: Mike Gould   Publisher: David Jamieson
Editor: Paul Martin   Cover design: Adam Wilmott
Cover illustration: Fabricio De Oliveira (Beehive Illustration)

Introduction

Welcome to Badger's **Under the Skin** Book 6!

These two challenging and stimulating plays are designed for enjoyment, but also to help students develop speaking and listening, drama and theatre skills. The series title - taken from one of the plays here - also gives a clue to their focus. They both cover a range of ideas, issues, stories and situations, but each is intended to uncover how and why individuals act in the way they do. Thus, they are plays designed with the stage and acting in mind, but can equally be enjoyed as group readers.

The plays were both written with an edge to them, but it is not the issues that drive them - rather an interest in telling a good story, with characters who engage our emotions and raise questions in our mind. Is Sykes wholly bad or can he be redeemed? What sort of friend is Su - the best or the worst type? Is Needle a Victorian villain or a devilish clown?

The plays are designed for small group performance or class reading, although it is recommended that, for the latter, one member of the group reads the stage directions and settings. Should you choose to perform the plays, much of the setting can be dispensed with, or presented in a stylised way, as in the end, it is the story and the words that matter - and you may interpret these as you wish.

All the plays in the series are written by people who are involved, or have been involved, in practical drama work with young people aged 11-16. They are an excellent resource to support the drama objectives in the Framework for Teaching English, and prepare students for drama study at GCSE and beyond, but more importantly, it is hoped that teachers and students will find them compelling and rewarding in their own right.

ICE MAIDEN

Characters:

LINUS	boy of about 12, small for age
SYKES	older boy of 16
KANE	boy of 14
BECKS	girl of 15
THE GIRL	18 or 19
THE WARDEN	man of about 45; Community Officer

ACT ONE

Scene 1   The garage

Darkness, then sudden lights up, as if a door has opened.

SYKES is sitting on a crate. He stands up.

SYKES: What took you?

A boy, KANE, and a girl, BECKS, move into the light.

BECKS: The Warden.

SYKES: (*suspicious*) What did he want?

BECKS: Nothing. We had to be friendly.

SYKES: And?

BECKS: Being friendly takes time...

SYKES: Hope you weren't too friendly.

KANE: (*suddenly, as if he hasn't been listening...*)
                  Here - see this Sykes...

He pulls a pack of playing cards out and offers one to SYKES.

SYKES: I haven't got time for...

KANE: (*giggling*) Go on, take one...

BECKS: Leave it Kane.

KANE: This is a good one!

SYKES grabs the cards and showers them on the ground.

SYKES: (*viciously*) Bet you haven't seen that one before!

KANE scrabbles around feverishly picking up the cards.

BECKS: Anyway, we're here now.

SYKES reaches behind the crate and pulls out a large carrier bag.

SYKES: Here.

BECKS looks inside and pulls out a football replica shirt.

BECKS: I don't believe it. Is this the real deal?

SYKES: Thirty quid in the shops. I've got a whole pile of them stashed at the back in those boxes. Birthday present.

BECKS: For me?

SYKES: No. My birthday.

BECKS: Oh. I didn't realise Sykes.

SYKES: They're the best type. Things you give yourself.

BECKS: You can't wear all of them.

SYKES: 'Course not. You can have one.

BECKS: Really? Cool.

SYKES: If you sell the rest. Should be a doddle. 15 quid a go. Take giggler with you.

KANE has finished scrabbling.

KANE: S-s-sykes...

SYKES: Another trick?

KANE: N-n-no. I can't find a card. The Queen of Spades. If you find it...

SYKES: Yeah - like I've got nothing to do.

SYKES moves towards the door.

SYKES: Turn the handle when you leave. Here!

He throws a key. KANE leaps up and catches it like a dog.

SYKES: Put the key through my old man's door. You know he can't answer it, being sick.

He leaves.

Scene 2   The Ring

This is the nickname for the circle of concrete surrounding a twisted steel modern sculpture designed during the estate's better days.

The same afternoon. Enter LINUS. He is hurrying, as if he doesn't want to be seen.

SYKES steps out from behind the sculpture.

SYKES: Oi, Minus. Where you going?

LINUS: Home, Sykes.

SYKES: What you got there?

LINUS: Nothing. Just a bag.

SYKES: An empty bag? Do you think I'm an idiot, Minus?

LINUS: Something for my mum. That's all.

SYKES: Here.

He grabs the bag and turns it upside down. Out fall several plastic containers for pills. They roll on the concrete.

SYKES bends down and picks one up. He hands it to LINUS.

SYKES: Read what it says.

LINUS: Err… Vitamin C.

SYKES grabs LINUS and pushes him against the structure.

SYKES: Just cos I can't read it don't mean I can't see. Vitamins always have bright colours. Those aren't vitamins. Now - tell me what's really on the label.

LINUS: 'Stilnox.'

SYKES: They're sleeping tablets. What's the other stuff?

LINUS: Things to make her feel better.

SYKES: (*laughs*) Cos you're her son?

LINUS: She gets anxious. Frightened of going out.

SYKES: Pick 'em up.

LINUS gathers the tablets up.

SYKES: Give 'em here.

LINUS: Sykes...

SYKES: Do it!

LINUS hands the tablets over.

SYKES: I'll have these. For now.

LINUS: (*desperate*) But she needs them, Sykes. She'll go mad.

SYKES: I said I'll keep 'em. Look after them.

LINUS: Please, Sykes.

SYKES: Alright. I'll tell you what I'll do. I need you to do something for me.

LINUS: What?

SYKES: I've been selected to collect something. Something important. From The Girl.

LINUS: The girl? What girl?

SYKES: Where you been, Minus?

LINUS: Sorry, Sykes. Things pass me by.

SYKES: How long you lived here?

LINUS: Twelve years, three months.

SYKES: And you don't know who I mean?

LINUS: (*uncertainly*) You mean Becks?

SYKES: Not Becks you doormat!

LINUS: Oh.

SYKES: (*he gestures offstage*) She's got a place in the basement. Or so they say. They say it's dead weird - all white and cold. No chairs, tables. Not even a TV. Used to be her parents' but they disappeared years ago. Some say she even killed them in their beds. That they're still there - buried under the floor.

LINUS: I thought you meant a real person.

SYKES: She is real.

LINUS: How do you know?

SYKES: They sent me a text.

He pulls out a flash flip-phone.

SYKES: Simple words. 'Go to The Girl.'

LINUS: Who sent it?

SYKES: I dunno. People. Someone important. I was selected.

LINUS: It doesn't mean she's real.

SYKES: Why would they send me to someone who wasn't real? What's the point of that?

LINUS: It doesn't say anything about collecting either.

SYKES: What else can it mean? That's what I do. I collect stuff. Then I pass it on. People give me money. That's how it works.

14

LINUS: It's good you've been selected.

SYKES: Don't be cute, Minus. I know what you think. You think I'm stupid. I can't read, can't hardly write. How long did you stay in school?

LINUS: I'm still there. Just not today. Cos of my mum.

SYKES: They chucked me out years ago.

LINUS: Why?

SYKES: You don't wanna know. Point is, it's me who got the text. Not you. Not Becks. Not Kane. Me.

LINUS: So, are you going to go?

SYKES: Yeah. But I want back-up.

LINUS: Me?

SYKES: If The Girl's a real nutcase then I want someone there.

LINUS: I'm not tough, Sykes, not like Becks.

SYKES: I need someone with brains, in case things get... complicated.

LINUS: Complicated?

SYKES: Girls are... it's different. You can't...

LINUS: Maybe she's not a girl. If no one's seen her.

SYKES: (*moves to the front of the stage*) I've seen her. In my dreams. She's blonde-haired - long - and she wears this dark, black dress and she's got like long pointy nails, and she speaks, but like some posh newsreader - not like us, and she lives underground so her eyes ain't too good...

-

LINUS: Sounds like a vampire...

SYKES: (*snapping out of his dream*) No - this ain't funny! Don't you make this funny!

LINUS: I'm sorry... I didn't mean...

SYKES: If this goes well, it could be the start of something. I don't wanna stay here all my life. I got to get away from...

He hesitates.

LINUS: From...?

SYKES: This. All this.

LINUS: And you'll give me the tablets back?

SYKES: I'll think about it.

LINUS: Please.

SYKES: Cross my heart.

LINUS: You should... I mean... go on then.

SYKES: What?

LINUS: It doesn't mean anything unless you do it, Sykes.

SYKES: (*angry*) You tellin' me what to do?

LINUS: No... it's just... just bad luck if you say it and don't do it.

SYKES: Bad luck?

LINUS: You don't want everything to go wrong, do you? I mean, seeing how you've been selected and all that...

SYKES: You're a nutter, Minus, you know that?

LINUS: (*almost smiles*) I know.

SYKES looks at LINUS a moment.

SYKES: OK.

He elaborately crosses himself.

SYKES: Cross my heart.

LINUS: And hope to die.

SYKES looks at him for a moment.

SYKES: Forget it. That's all you're getting from me.

He moves towards the side of the stage.

SYKES: Let's go, Minus.

LINUS follows him.

Scene 3   The Ring

Early evening. Lights up on THE WARDEN. He's carrying a torch. The following rhyme/rap is done at increasing pace and should end with the Warden at the top of the sculpture, holding his torch outstretched, casting a beam into the sky.

WARDEN: They call me The Warden and I'm no cop,
But this is my turf and when I say 'stop',
You got to turn and tell me your name and place,
Cos when it comes to crime I can memorise a face.

Cos I'm the Warden of the Flats and the Warden of the Ring,
I move like a cat, don't stop for anything,
This is my day-job, my night-job, my hopes and dreams,
In this concrete jungle, I'm the real lion king.

When I came here, the crime was high,
But now I have my fingers in everybody's pies,
They can't move an inch without me seeing it all,
I have ears in the ceilings and eyes in the walls.

WARDEN: Cos I'm the Warden of the Flats and the Warden of the Ring,
I move like a cat, don't stop for anything,
This is my day-job, my night-job, my hopes and dreams,
In this concrete jungle, I'm the real lion king.

I know them all, from Kane to Sykes,
From Linus and his mum, to the kid who nicks bikes,
From the winos and the tramps,
To the girl called Becks.

They know me too, and wish me dead,
Cos I see into their lives, I make all the rules,
I report them to their mothers, and also to their schools,
I stop them having fun and I stop them doing stuff,
Unless they pay, I go in rough.

Cos I'm the Warden of the Flats and the Warden of the Ring,
I move like a cat, don't stop for anything,
This is my day-job, my night-job, my hopes and dreams,
In this concrete jungle, I'm the real lion king!

He jumps down from the sculpture.

WARDEN: Thing is, I know that scumbag Sykes is up to something. And if he is, I want a part of it.

How do you think I keep this place the way I want? Do you think I do it by being Mr Nice Guy? By telling the nice little police force what's going on?

WAKE UP and smell the COFFEE!

NO. This is my patch. They wouldn't have me in the police. Said I was a 'liability'. Too rough. Too nasty. Too... good at my job, maybe!

But, here. I do what I want. I let Sykes get on with his dodgy stuff - as long as I get something out of it.

He pulls something out from inside his jacket. It's a replica shirt.

That girl Becks was selling 'em for 15 quid all over the estate. Fifteen quid? That's downright criminal. Funny thing was - she gave me this one for NOTHING! Lovely Christmas present for a mate.

WARDEN: Wait a minute. Someone's coming...
              someone entering my little den.

*He switches the torch off and bounds to the top of the
sculpture.*

Enter KANE.

KANE: I must... I have to... perhaps it's... I
              m-m-might have dropped it...

He scrabbles on the ground.

KANE: It's S-s-sykes fault. I hate him, I hate him, I
              HATE him!

WARDEN: (*aside*) Interesting, very interesting. Let's
              hear more.

KANE: The Queen of Sp-sp-sp-spades. Just one
              little c-c-card. But I can't do anything
              without it.

              And now Sykes has gone down with Linus
              to see her...

WARDEN: Her? Who does he mean?

KANE: And she'll destroy them. She'll make mincemeat of them. She doesn't have anything to give them. It's a b-b-big fat lie. A trap. A trick. So they'll never come back. And then I'll never find it.

I'll check again. Perhaps I missed it.

KANE squats down on the floor and pulls out the card pack and starts placing the cards one by one on top of each other, reading each one aloud. This continues as the WARDEN speaks.

KANE: Three of Diamonds, Jack of Hearts, Four of Clubs, Seven of Clubs...

WARDEN: So, they've gone somewhere. "Down" he said. Hmmm. I smell a rat - named Sykes. And a 'girl'. Who can that be? Well, we shall find out more...

He suddenly turns his torch beam on KANE.

KANE sprawls back in fear.

In a bound, the WARDEN is on the ground again. He points the beam directly at a prostrate KANE.

WARDEN: Well, young Kane. So, you hate your friend Sykes, do you?

KANE: N-n-n-nooo.

WARDEN: Oh yes. I heard it most clearly. Now where would Sykes and Linus be?

KANE: I don't know. I p-p-p-promise...

WARDEN: Oh, I think you do know, Kane.

Moves closer until he is pointing the torch beam direct into KANE's eyes.

KANE: Don't! It hurts!

WARDEN: Well then. Tell me. Tell me where they've gone.

KANE: I can't. I swore. Said I wouldn't.

WARDEN: I said "TELL ME"!

KANE: No... I... Please...

WARDEN: I have something for you.

He takes something slowly out of his pocket and holds it up.

KANE: The Queen of Sp-sp-sp-spades! W-w-where...

WARDEN: It's yours. Just give me the low-down. On Linus and Sykes. Where they were going.

KANE: (*staring at the card*) Is it really mine...?

WARDEN: Tell me first.

KANE: Let me see the card.

WARDEN: There.

He holds it up.

KANE: It's the only one missing.

WARDEN: Come on, Kane. The girl. Which girl?

KANE: (*slowly*) Her.

WARDEN: Oh, very helpful. Say goodbye to the Queen...

He makes to tear the card.

KANE: (*panicky*) The Girl! You know... the one who...

WARDEN: Spit it out...

KANE: ...in the basement.

WARDEN: Her? She doesn't exist. That's just a story made up by parents to scare their kids. There is no room - no basement.

KANE: There was a message.

WARDEN: What message?

KANE: They didn't say. But they've gone.

WARDEN: (*with a flash of his hand*) Like your card. (*the card has disappeared*) Gone.

He turns off the torch.

Instant blackout.

ACT TWO

Scene 1   The basement room

The same day, much later. Lights up to reveal LINUS and SYKES in a clean, white room with no windows. There are three pure white computers with flat screens, humming but with no images. There is one shelf running along a wall. On it there are CDs/DVDs, wires, bits of kit and a silver photo-frame. A couple of functional chairs of stainless steel are to one side.

SYKES: Just came right in - not exactly Wormwood Scrubs, is it?

LINUS: (*quiet*) It's not getting in we have to worry about.

SYKES: (*not listening*) All those years I used to go down that lift. Never realised there was a button under 'Ground Floor'.

LINUS: Perhaps it wasn't there.

SYKES: (*turning*) You what?

LINUS: I mean… I never noticed it either.

SYKES: Nah. It was there, alright. Just we weren't looking.

SYKES walks around gazing at all the kit.

SYKES: Must have cost a fortune, this lot.

LINUS: Don't touch it, Sykes.

SYKES: Why not?

LINUS: I don't know. What you going to do with computers? You hate them, you told me.

SYKES: 'Course I hate 'em. Just more stuff to understand. Best to keep things simple, but even I know that top kit like this costs a fortune.

LINUS: Might not be new.

SYKES: Do me a favour. Does it look old? Nah - this is state of the art.

LINUS: But it belongs to someone.

SYKES: There's no one here. I could take this lot in half-an-hour. Give Becks a call - and that idiot, Kane.

LINUS: Of course there's someone here.

SYKES: Look around, Minus. There ain't no other doors. No, it'll be here somewhere - the stuff I'm supposed to collect.

Suddenly, as if he's had a brainwave.

That's it!

LINUS: What?

SYKES: This lot. (*he gestures at the computers*) This is what I'm supposed to collect. It ain't nothing to do with a girl.

LINUS: But you said you'd seen her - in your dreams.

SYKES: I was being stupid. Not thinking straight. This is just some computer storage place. The message meant I could walk right in. Nick the stuff, then they'll collect it from me at the garage.

LINUS: They? Who?

SYKES: I dunno, do I? People. Movers, shakers.

He pulls out his mobile and flicks open the screen. He thumbs a button or two.

SYKES: Becks? Yeah, it's me, Sykesy. Look, grab Kane and get yourself to the lift in A Block. I got something I need a hand with. Press the button under 'G'. No - it's not marked or anything. Right, and be quick.

He puts the mobile away.

Sorted. She's on her way.

LINUS: This is a mistake, Sykes.

SYKES grabs LINUS.

SYKES: No, Minus. You're the mistake. I didn't need you after all.

He pushes him into one of the chairs.

Now, sit still like a good boy while I have a look at this kit.

SYKES goes round the room, peering at the wires, prodding the equipment until he comes to the shelf and the DVD/CDs. He glances at the first few.

SYKES: All blank - just got numbers on 190804, 230303...

He stops at the photo.

SYKES: What's this? Some old photo with kids in. Bit faint. Frame's well heavy - must be solid silver.

LINUS: You don't need to take that...

SYKES: What's it to you?

LINUS: Can I see it?

SYKES: I found it. You're not having it.

LINUS: I just want a look. You always said I had a good memory - I might recognise them.

SYKES: Alright. A couple of seconds then I want it back.

SYKES hands it to LINUS, who has stood up. He looks at it a moment, then a change comes over his face.

SYKES: What's the matter, Minus? You gone all pale.

LINUS: (*faltering*) Nothing, Sykes. It's...

SYKES: You know these people?

LINUS: No. I mean, yes.

SYKES: Very clear.

LINUS: I don't know.

SYKES: Make your mind up.

LINUS: I did.

SYKES: Did?

LINUS: They're dead.

SYKES: You mean, this really is that girl's place?

LINUS: What?

SYKES: You know what they said. Killed her parents.

LINUS: That's just a story.

SYKES: Oh yeah. They could be holed up behind these walls.

He laughs and prods a wall.

Is anyone there?

LINUS: Stop it, Sykes.

SYKES: Anyway, don't make no difference. Dead can't hurt you. Now - give me that frame.

LINUS: Please, Sykes.

SYKES: You heard me.

LINUS: No.

SYKES: What did you say?

LINUS: I... can't.

SYKES: I said, "GIMME THAT FRAME"!

LINUS: Take the computers, the DVDs. Anything. But not this.

SYKES: That's it. I've had it with you.

He pulls out a flick-knife and advances towards LINUS.

           Now, gimme that frame or...

Suddenly the lights get brighter and there is a sudden fizz or crackle of electricity.

SYKES cries out in pain and twists and curls as if he has been given an electric shock. He drops the knife and falls to the floor.

Blackout.

Scene 2   The basement room

Slow lights up on the same room. A dimmer, blue light. Cold. SYKES is in a chair, hands bound behind him. LINUS is nowhere to be seen.

Slowly, from the shadow at the side of the stage, a figure emerges. It is a GIRL. She is tall, dressed in a white all-in-one suit, rather like a nuclear worker. Even her shoes are white. She is pale and her face is unnaturally white.

SYKES: (*almost sobbing*) What did you do to me?

The GIRL doesn't answer, just moves around the room. She touches a few buttons on the keyboards and all the screens simultaneously show SYKES in his chair.

SYKES: You were watching. You knew all the time.

The GIRL takes the other chair and pulls it right up close to SYKES. Then she sits down and leans forward. She reaches out her hand and clasps SYKES' chin.

SYKES: Don't... not like before...

GIRL: Don't speak.

She releases his face.

You'll live.

34

SYKES: Who...?

The GIRL wags her finger.

GIRL: No questions.

SYKES: I'm cold. It's freezing in here.

GIRL: Is it? I hadn't noticed.

She goes over to the computers and holds a DVD up.

201294. Ring any bells?

SYKES: No. Just a stupid number.

GIRL: 20th December 1994.

SYKES: I can't remember that. I was...

GIRL: ...a child?

SYKES: Yeah.

He twists in his chair.

Please. Let me go - I'm freezing to death here!

GIRL: Yes, you are.

SYKES: Where's Linus? What you done with him?

GIRL: (*ignoring him*) Doesn't seem cold to me.

SYKES: They'll be coming for me.

GIRL: (*to herself*) I always hated the sun. From that day.

SYKES: What day?

GIRL: It was like summer. I hated that. December was supposed to be cold. December was meant to be ice. Snow. Frost.

SYKES: What are you talking about?

GIRL: But that day - when you and your brothers came by...

SYKES: Me? My brothers? What they got to do with anything?

GIRL: 1994.

SYKES: My brothers are in jail. I ain't seen them in years.

GIRL: You were too young.

SYKES: Who *are* you?

36

GIRL: The three of you, with those fireworks.

SYKES: (*sobbing, beginning to realise*) They got punished. Kicked off the estate.

GIRL: You didn't.

SYKES: I was just a little kid. A silly kid! You can't...

GIRL: My mother got burnt down her face. Scarred. My father didn't want to stay when he saw how she looked. Lucky the little one didn't get it really. I looked for ice, snow, anything to soothe my mother's face but it was too late.

SYKES: I didn't throw anything.

GIRL: And that's when it started.

SYKES: It was you in the flat. In that photo, too.

GIRL: My skin rejected the sun. Must have been the shock. Rejected heat, too.

SYKES: It was meant to be a joke.

GIRL: After your brothers' trial I had to move away. Get treatment.

SYKES: You came back.

GIRL: There are no windows here. Except these.

She gestures at the screens.

They see everything.

SYKES: Everything?

GIRL: You. That girl. Kane. The Warden.

She picks up a handful of DVDs/CDs and throws them viciously on the floor in front of SYKES.

Everything you've done, every scam, every nasty trick, every punch and kick...

SYKES: I was just trying to get by. You don't know what it's like with him watching...

GIRL: The Warden.

SYKES: Yeah.

GIRL: There's always someone to blame.

SYKES: What you gonna do?

GIRL: (*hardly listening*) I waited till you were 16. Till I knew you were old enough to go to jail for a long time.

SYKES: My birthday.

GIRL: (*harsh*) A little present for you.

SYKES: How did you...?

GIRL: Technology's easy when you can't go outside. Hours and hours while they treated my skin. They gave me a laptop to play games on. Soon, I'd learnt how to access the CCTV in the hospital. It was easy once I'd come back here. And found myself this old basement room. Plugged into the estate cameras and now I've got months of evidence transferred onto High Density DVD.

SYKES: I'm sorry.

GIRL: Too late.

SYKES: Let me go. I don't care what the cops do.

GIRL: Maybe you'll get away with everything you've done.

SYKES: I'll plead guilty. Tell 'em I've turned over a new leaf.

GIRL: (*bitterly*) New leaves don't exist. Just shrivelled up old ones.

SYKES: I promise.

GIRL: No - I've changed my mind.

SYKES: What?

GIRL: Now the time's come. Prison's too good.

SYKES: (*panicky*) I don't understand.

GIRL: We're leaving.

SYKES: You and me?

GIRL: Me and Linus.

SYKES: Linus?

GIRL: Work it out.

SYKES: If I stay here, I'll freeze to death.

GIRL: Yes.

She starts packing up. Puts the photo frame into a rucksack.

SYKES: You said you can't go outside.

GIRL: It's all sorted. A car's coming. A special one with tinted glass. We're going north.

SYKES: Please!

The GIRL continues to pack stuff away.

SYKES: Don't leave me!

The GIRL goes to the door, turns and looks once at SYKES. Then leaves.

Fade lights.

Scene 3   Empty space

The stage is bare.

Enter LINUS stage left and the GIRL stage right. They stand facing each other across the stage.

LINUS: You.

GIRL: Yes.

LINUS: You said you'd come back.

GIRL: I did.

LINUS: I never visited you.

GIRL: I didn't want people.

LINUS: It's cold here.

GIRL: Not to me.

LINUS: Will we stay?

GIRL: No, we'll go.

LINUS: Where to?

GIRL: Where there's snow.

LINUS: And ice?

GIRL: And Christmas trees.

LINUS: And lights?

GIRL: Not too bright.

They walk towards each other.

LINUS: Is it over?

GIRL: Not yet.

LINUS: Not yet?

GIRL: Soon.

LINUS raises his hand to touch her cheek.

LINUS: Your face has changed.

GIRL: Everything's changed...

LINUS: The ice melts.

GIRL: Not yet.

LINUS: No, not yet.

Fade lights.

Scene 4   Outside the basement room

BECKS and KANE are pushed into the light. The WARDEN follows.

WARDEN: Go on, then.

BECKS: We ain't never been here before.

WARDEN: (*sarcastic*) 'Course you haven't. This where you store all your stuff?

KANE: N-n-nooo.

BECKS: I tell you, we just got a message.

WARDEN: I knew Sykes had somewhere. He knows the rules. I get 60% of everything he makes. Pills, potions, trainers, shirts.

BECKS: It's the truth. They told him to come.

WARDEN: They? Don't give me that. He only takes orders from me.

He prods BECKS towards the side of the stage.

There's the door. You go in.

At that moment, LINUS enters from where the door might be.

WARDEN: Ah, our little friend, Linus. We too late to catch Sykes with his stuff?

LINUS: (*calmly*) There's no point going in.

WARDEN: What you on about, you little squirt?

LINUS: It's over.

WARDEN: (*growing anger*) What's "over"?

LINUS pulls out a DVD.

What's that?

The WARDEN grabs it and looks at it.

Just got a number. 201294.

LINUS: 20th December.

WARDEN: (*uneasily*) This is just a DVD.

LINUS: Did you know we had CCTV here in '94? One of the first estates in the country.

WARDEN: So?

LINUS: There's video on there. Some bloke selling illegal fireworks to kids.

WARDEN: Happens all the time. People have to make a living.

LINUS: The problem is, this sale almost led to someone dying.

WARDEN: Well, I got it now. Can't do much with it, can you?

LINUS: That's a copy. The original's been sent by email to the police.

WARDEN: One image is pretty useless. Can't identify people.

LINUS: Oh, didn't I say? That's just one of many. There's hours on there. Then there's 050699. That's a good one. Some man just like you removing a mountain bike from one of the flats. Then there's 170202, the same man selling prescription drugs to some young girls by the garages. Then there's 060803, an assault, 300999, 020401...

WARDEN: You're joking. It wasn't me...

LINUS: Of course not.

WARDEN: I can prove...

LINUS: (*steadily*) You're finished.

WARDEN: (*colour draining*) I... if Sykes is behind this, I'll kill... he's... I mean...

LINUS: There's nothing left for you.

WARDEN: The girl. This is her doing.

LINUS: There is no girl. Just a storeroom full of CDs.

In the distance we hear the wail of a police siren.

WARDEN: I'll get you... all of you...

He turns and rushes off.

LINUS picks up something from the floor. It is a card.

KANE: The Queen!

BECKS: What's going on? None of this makes any sense. What's this about a girl? Where's Sykes?

LINUS: He'll turn up.

BECKS: But there was a message.

LINUS: It was all a mistake. There was just a room. With DVDs. Undercover police maybe.

BECKS: No more cheap pills and trainers?

LINUS: Probably not.

BECKS: What'll happen to Sykes?

LINUS: I don't know.

BECKS: It doesn't seem possible.

LINUS: The door's locked. Try it if you want.

BECKS goes over and pushes.

BECKS: We better go. Before the police arrive. Will we be alright?

LINUS: No one's interested in us.

BECKS and KANE leave.

LINUS goes to the door and slowly knocks three times.

He exits.

Scene 5   The basement room

Enter LINUS. SYKES is still on the chair. He is very still.

SYKES: (*almost inaudible*) Minus.

LINUS: I'm going Sykes.

SYKES: You can't. I'll...

LINUS: I have to.

SYKES: You don't.

LINUS: I do.

SYKES: You can tell her. She'll listen to you.

LINUS: What?

SYKES: She's your sister.

LINUS: It's too late.

SYKES: I was a KID!

LINUS: I was a baby. She saved me. But she couldn't save Mum's face. Why do you think Mum needs those pills?

SYKES: You can have them back.

49

LINUS: Doesn't matter. We're all leaving. Going where you and your father can't get us.

SYKES: My old man?

LINUS: Yes.

SYKES: What's he got to do with it?

LINUS: I know who he is.

SYKES: Don't play games.

LINUS: Always thought it was strange we never saw your father.

SYKES: He was ill.

LINUS: Was?

SYKES: Is. I mean 'is'.

LINUS: He isn't lying in his bed in that flat. All those years, you and him, making our lives hell. When I found out just now, it all made sense.

SYKES: What was I supposed to do? My own dad. It was his idea to become a warden on the estate.

LINUS: Who was he in 1994? Not the Warden.

SYKES: He sold us the fireworks. His own kids. Didn't even give them to us.

LINUS: You were four years old.

SYKES: We didn't know he was our dad. Just a bloke who came to Mum's flat for cash and food.

LINUS: No one knew.

SYKES: Then he told me. Once he'd become the Warden. Persuaded the police he'd gone straight. All these years he's controlled me, made me do stuff.

LINUS: I've got to go.

LINUS moves towards the door.

SYKES: I'll die! If the cold doesn't get me, he will.

LINUS: I was never here.

SYKES: I'm still a kid!

LINUS: You're sixteen. How could you forget your own birthday?

SYKES: I'm begging you.

At that moment, the GIRL comes in.

LINUS: I thought you were waiting outside.

GIRL: Couldn't stand the light, so I came back to fetch you.

She goes over to the wall and adjusts a dial.

SYKES: Don't make it colder!

GIRL: 13 degrees.

SYKES: What does she mean?

GIRL: Warm enough to live. Like a mild winter's day.

LINUS: She's turned it up.

The GIRL comes over and looks at SYKES.

GIRL: Your father's finished.

SYKES: How can he be?

GIRL: Don't be a fool.

SYKES looks at LINUS.

LINUS: The police took him away.

SYKES: (*to the GIRL*) When did you find out he was the Warden?

GIRL: The moment I saw him on the screen of my computer. That face of his has been burned into my mind from the day I left here.

SYKES: So, you've always known?

GIRL: Since I came back. Yes.

She undoes him. SYKES is so cold he can hardly stand.

SYKES: (*can't believe she's releasing him*) You're letting me go...? I thought...

GIRL: You want to stay there?

SYKES: No.

GIRL: Here.

She hands him a pile of DVDs/CDs. He half-gathers them in his arms.

SYKES: What's this?

GIRL: Your life.

SYKES is speechless for a moment, turning the DVDs over in his hand.

SYKES: I thought you didn't believe in new leaves.

GIRL: Not for me.

She turns to LINUS.

But there are always other people.

She takes his hand. They leave.

SYKES is left in the middle of the stage, shivering, holding the DVDs.

Slowly fade lights.

The door slams shut.

UNDER THE SKIN

Characters:

BOY	aged about 17
GIRL/JO	schoolgirl, 15
NEEDLE	a man, age unimportant
LENA	girl, 15
SU	girl, 15
KIT	boy, 14, Su's younger brother
DANIELLA	schoolgirl, 15

The stage remains the same throughout. Downstage right, a roundabout from a children's park. The back wall suggests the front of a shop, with a door to one side. A dull light glows in the back of it as this scene begins.

No other set.

Scene 1

Enter a BOY and a GIRL.

GIRL: This it, Robbie - can we go in?

BOY: Why? What's the hurry?

GIRL: You promised.

BOY: I said I didn't mind. It's not the same thing.

GIRL: Well. Can we go in?

BOY peers through window.

BOY: It's not open.

GIRL: There's a light.

BOY: We'll come back another time. It's late.

GIRL: Someone's coming.

Enter NEEDLE. He comes from the shop.

NEEDLE: Are you good people intending to enter my establishment?

GIRL: You what?

56

BOY: No - you're alright mate. We're just off.

NEEDLE: Not so fast, not so anxious. Let me guess...

He looks them up and down.

              A heart and two names? No, not your
              style...

GIRL: I'd like that, it sounds...

BOY: (*interrupting*) Shut up!

NEEDLE: Or letters on each knuckle? Wouldn't suit
              you, I fear... Let me see, let me see...

BOY: C'mon...

GIRL: I want to stay.

NEEDLE: But, wait a minute. Haven't I seen you
              before?

BOY: We gotta go.

NEEDLE: I never forget someone's skin.

GIRL: (*to the BOY*) You've been here before?

NEEDLE: Last week.

BOY: You got the wrong bloke, mate.

NEEDLE: (*to the GIRL*) Your beloved was my canvas.

GIRL: You have been here before! You told me I was special.

BOY: You are! It's not that...

NEEDLE: Now - what was her name?

GIRL: Her name?

BOY: You don't understand.

NEEDLE: Yes - I recall it now. Just by your heart. Seven letters or nine...

GIRL: You said I'd be the first. That my name...

BOY: (*desperate*) It don't matter... He can add yours.

GIRL: Add it?

BOY: It ain't no big deal. Your name can go underneath. Or on my arm, or on my hand...

NEEDLE: I remember. It began with a 'C' and an 'H'...

GIRL: Charlotte? That cow down the café? You
             swore you didn't fancy her!

BOY: I don't!

GIRL: I knew she was after you.

BOY: It's nothing to do with her!

GIRL: Yeah? Well prove it.

BOY: What?

NEEDLE: I think the young lady means that you
             should demonstrate the evidence.

GIRL: That's it. Evidence. If you've got something
             on your skin, you better show me.

BOY: Alright, alright! Then you'll be happy?

GIRL: Whatever.

He hesitates.

             Go on, then. What you waitin' for?

*He tears off his shirt and reveals his chest. The audience
can't see it, but NEEDLE and the GIRL can.*

BOY: See! That's all it is!

59

The GIRL backs away, horrified.

GIRL: This is a joke.

BOY: (*proud*) Nice, innit? Classy. I mean, I wanted you first, but the lads...

GIRL: The lads?

BOY: They persuaded me. It had to be the Blues. That's why it's all in blue.

GIRL: Blue?

BOY steps forward.

BOY: See? It's their colour. Chelsea. (*spells it out*) C-H-E-L-S-E-A F.C. Nine letters.

GIRL: (*astounded*) You chose a football team before me?

BOY: Come on, babe. Not any football team.

GIRL: I don't believe this.

BOY: Look - you can have any design you want. On me or on you. I'll pay.

She looks at him with barely concealed disgust.

BOY: You choose. A rose, a tree. Even a snake.
               They cost loads.

NEEDLE: A snake would be very appropriate.

GIRL: I don't want anything from you.

She turns and goes.

BOY: Wait up!

GIRL: (*turns*) Forget it, Robbie. It's too late.

She leaves.

NEEDLE: Are you coming in, sir?

BOY: (*low*) She's gone. Not much point.

NEEDLE: Oh, there's always a point.

BOY: I should go after her.

NEEDLE: We close soon.

*BOY hesitates. Looks in the direction the GIRL has
exited. Then turns back.*

BOY: There is something.

NEEDLE: Yes?

BOY: Could you do me a bridge?

NEEDLE: Ah! A bridge over troubled waters!

BOY: No, mate.

NEEDLE: Perhaps the Bridge of Sighs. Venice. City of romance. Most appealing.

BOY: What're you on? Nah - Stamford Bridge. It's where they play.

NEEDLE: Your wish is my command.

He holds open the door.

Enter!

The BOY goes in, followed by NEEDLE, who shuts the door behind him.

Slowly the light in the shop goes out.

Scene 2

Lights up on LENA on the roundabout, feet dangling. It moves slowly. KIT stands watching her.

LENA: I told you. I'm not doing it.

KIT: She only...

LENA: (*interrupting*) No. It's not right. Why should I?

KIT: No one'll see it.

LENA: I'll see it. And there's my mum.

KIT: She'll get over it.

LENA gets off the roundabout and spins it violently.

LENA: It's a test, that's what it is.

KIT: She's your best mate.

LENA: Why're you defending her? You've slagged her off plenty of times.

KIT: That's what brothers are supposed to do. Besides, she's kinda changed.

LENA: How d'you mean?

63

KIT: Like she's...

LENA: (*interrupting*) You can't get at her.

KIT: That's right! She's like this ice cold wall. Nothing touches her.

LENA: Exactly... but it's like she owns me.

KIT: Me too.

KIT comes over and sits on the roundabout.

Where is she, anyway? Thought she'd be here by now.

LENA: I'm going, before she comes.

KIT: You can't run away.

LENA: Why not?

KIT: Err. Don't know. You just can't.

LENA: Watch me.

Before LENA can leave, SU enters.

SU: Hiya girlfriend.

LENA: Hi yourself.

64

SU: What's up? You look like you swallowed a sour lemon.

LENA: It's nothing, Su. Look, I'm just off.

KIT: Are you?

LENA: Yes. My mum wants me to stop by the shops, get some bread and stuff.

SU: Charming!

LENA: I'll text you later.

LENA turns to go.

SU: Hey Lena!

LENA stops.

SU: Have you thought about it?

LENA: What?

SU: You know.

LENA: Remind me.

SU: Our tattoo.

LENA says nothing.

SU: So? What d'you say?

KIT remains on the roundabout, gently rocking.

LENA: I don't know.

SU: Just you and me, and the girls. Like it's
               always been. Since primary school. Best
               mates. But you especially.

LENA: Look...

SU: I just knew from the start. And I know that
               in ten years time, twenty years, we'll still be
               mates.

LENA: Why's this so important?

SU: We're bound to go our separate ways when
               school ends, so we should make a vow.

LENA: What do you mean?

SU: A blood vow.

LENA: Blood?

SU: A vow that whatever happens, whoever we
               marry, divorce, end up with, you, me and
               the others will meet. At the top of the
               Blackpool Tower. Or on the London Eye.
               Wherever. In ten years time.

LENA: It'd be good to meet up.

SU: But we need to seal the vow. That's why we need a tattoo. Just a tiny little one. With all our names.

LENA: I'm not sure.

SU: 'Course you're not. It's a big step committing yourself to your mates.

LENA: I'll think about it.

SU: Good girl.

She links arms with LENA.

SU: C'mon. I can help you with your shopping.

KIT: What about me? What am I gonna do?

SU: We got girls' stuff to discuss.

KIT: So?

SU: So run along home like a good little boy and tell Dad I'll be home soon.

They leave.

KIT: Great.

Lights slowly up on the shop front. KIT walks towards it and peers into the window.

KIT: Blimey. Dragons. That one's dead weird.

He twists his head as if trying to make sense of it.

That's disgusting!

Moves along a bit and looks again.

Cool! On my neck or arm? Arm definitely. That way, everytime I looked at my watch, everyone would see.

Suddenly, the door opens and NEEDLE emerges.

NEEDLE: Good evening, young sir. See anything you like? Perhaps an eagle or an anchor? A sword or a skull?

KIT backing away.

KIT: No... err... I was just looking...

NEEDLE moves towards him.

NEEDLE: A lion or a leopard? A knight or a ninja? A shield or a...

KIT's mobile suddenly rings.

KIT: Oh, hi Dad. Yeah - just on my way back. I'm with Su - it's alright.

NEEDLE: Another time, perhaps?

KIT stares at the shop and the window for a moment, and then turns and runs off.

NEEDLE returns to the shop. As he gets to the door, the BOY emerges.

BOY: Thanks, mate.

He peers down inside his shirt.

That's the business, that!

He walks off.

NEEDLE: Another happy customer.

Lights down.

Scene 3

Enter LENA, on her own.

LENA: Suddenly we're all talking about it at
school. At least Su and the rest are. What's
worse, they want the predictable ones; you
know - love hearts, a twisted, thorny rose, a
name... on the top of their arms, their
backs, their thighs. They won't stop going
on about it.

I'd never understood that stupid phrase
'peer pressure' until now. Cos I've always
wanted to do what my mates wanted to do
before. But this time it's different.

Don't get me wrong - it isn't because I don't
like the look of tattoos. I mean I can think
of other things I'd prefer - like bigger boobs
or straighter hair. But I'm not against them
because they look crap. Even I can see on
some people they look alright. Kinda cool.
It's just that the more Su and the others go
on, the more this little feeling creeps up on
me, bit by bit, like the shadow of the moon.

And all of a sudden I need that light over
me, cos my own friends are like strangers. I
mean, after school, when we come down
here they're people I don't know. Yet I'm not
surprised. It's like I've been expecting it.

Enter JO.

LENA: First there's Jo.

JO: It'll look cool. Do you good. You need...
something.

Freeze JO, arms folded, staring in at LENA.

LENA: (*aside*) Typical Jo. Giving a compliment
with one hand, stabbing with another.

Enter DANI.

Then, there's Daniella. No pretence there.
Just straight to the point.

DANI: You know something, Lena? You're a right
boring cow. You don't get yourself a tattoo,
it's like you're scared. Who's gonna care?
Not worried about what your mum'll say,
are you? She's boring, too. D'you wanna be
like her?

DANI freezes in the same pose as JO.

LENA: I think about a reply, even about hitting
her, but by the time I line it up, the
moment's gone. Suddenly it makes me
wonder what I see in them all.

Enter SU.

LENA: But the worst is Su. My best mate. Susannah. Susie-Sue. My soul mate. The one person I thought I really might still be friends with when I'm drawing my pension. The person I'd give anything up for. The sister I never had.

People say we're joined at the hip. We even look alike. A kind of symmetry between us. Balance, call it what you will.

And here we are, outside 'Skin Deep'.

SU: What d'you reckon, then, Lena? Did you have a think about what I said last night?

LENA: Nah. Not my thing. (*aside to audience*) I say this casually, I hope.

SU: We not good enough for you?

LENA: No, it's not that. Can't explain really. Just don't fancy having it done. It's too... I dunno... permanent. (*aside, to the audience*) ...and then, the sucker punch. The test.

SU: But you'd do it if I had it done, wouldn't you, Lena?

All three girls stare at LENA, arms folded.

LENA: What?

SU: I said, you'd do it if I did, wouldn't you...?

LENA turns to the audience. The others freeze.

LENA: The question hangs in the air.

                I realise then what friendship is all about. It's not about affection or love, or support. It's about allegiance. Whose side you are on.

SU comes 'back to life'.

SU: Can't let Jo and Dani down, can we?

                A little one wouldn't do any harm. We could all have the same one. A tiny starfish. Names at the end of each tentacle.

LENA: Starfish have five tentacles.

SU: One for today's date, then.

LENA: I don't feel good about this.

SU: (*pressing*) We'd be like the four musketeers...

LENA: They were blokes.

SU: Same difference. Then ten years time on the London Eye, or at the top of the Eiffel Tower, like I said, we could meet up.

LENA: You said Blackpool.

SU: The place doesn't matter. It's the tattoo that counts. Cos it will always be there. To remind us where we came from. Remind us who we are.

SU freezes, arms folded. LENA turns to audience.

LENA: It's quite a speech from Su. Then I think about ten years' time. What I'll be doing, who I'll be with. And I suddenly see a life without them. Without teenage allegiance.

         After all, I hadn't chosen any of them. When my parents split up, I'd gone with my mum. I was new at the school. Year 8. And when I arrived they chose me. Adopted me. Selected me. Which was great, cos that's better than the alternative.

         But then, as I think about friendship and allegiance, I remember something else. This programme we saw at school - about the holocaust a few weeks ago.

She joins the other three, and they move and sit together on the roundabout.

Slowly, a light comes up near the shop, as if the front is the screen.

JO: This is dead boring, this. It's all in black and white.

DANI: More like brown.

LENA: Wait a mo - what's that about?

A MAN appears, shaved head bowed, walking slowly in front of them. Another man, possibly NEEDLE but not obviously so, steps out. The MAN holds his arm out, head still down. NEEDLE rolls up the MAN's sleeve and mimes branding his forearm. He reacts, screaming wordlessly in pain.

SU: Did you see that? That's... disgusting.

LENA: They're branding them with numbers. Just like cattle.

DANI: How d'you know, smart-ass?

LENA: Our history teacher told us at my last school.

SU: They shouldn't make us watch stuff like this. It's too depressing. You've got to enjoy yourselves now. Live for today.

The three girls freeze on the roundabout, but LENA stands up. The two men go.

LENA: The programme was over, but the man wouldn't go away. I saw him... still see him... Thing is, he was stuck with that number and short of cutting off a limb, he'd always be that prisoner, always defined by one moment of searing heat.

Of course I know mine will just be a tattoo. Silly to get so worked up about it. A harmless little one probably. And maybe nowadays the needle won't burn so much.

But I don't want to be defined by them. (*she gestures to SU and the others*) By my need to form an allegiance with them. So I tell them...

She turns to the three girls.

You go ahead. I can't do it.

SU stands up and walks up to LENA. She faces her for a moment as if she might hit her.

The other two stand up too, and walk over to the shop, standing on either side of the door.

LENA: (*aside to the audience*) Then, Su speaks.

SU: Nah, Lena's right.

She passes by LENA.

It's a stupid idea... You get one if you want, Dani. And you too, Jo. It'll suit you both. You and David Beckham.

She laughs, almost cruelly.

JO: But, you said...

SU: I never meant it. Not for me and Lena.

DANI: What about all that stuff about meeting in ten years' time? About this being a way of remembering?

SU: You don't wanna believe everything I say. You need brains, like Lena.

JO: What we gonna do? I psyched myself up for this.

SU: Why don't you ask Robbie? You know - love-hearts and all that.

JO: Yeah, I could do that. What d'you reckon, Dani?

DANI: (*bitter*) I didn't want no stupid tattoo anyway. I suppose you wanna go round lover-boy's?

JO: D'you mind?

DANI: S'pose not.

They leave.

SU: Fancy an ice-cream?

LENA: That'd be nice.

SU: Come on. I'll treat you.

SU walks to the side of the stage and looks briefly at LENA.

SU: And on the way, you can tell me the real reason you didn't want a tattoo, can't you?

SU leaves.

LENA: And she walks off, expecting me to catch her up. And I know I've built this first wall between us. Or perhaps she has.